Lil' Sass and The Adventure of Anger

Written by Christie Mann

Lil' Sass Explores her Emotions and Learns
that it's OK to Express Anger

Dedication & Acknowledgements

For all the little hearts in my life, watching you grow is one of my greatest joys, and it inspired me to write this series.
And for your mothers and fathers—because without them, you would not be here and Sass would not have been birthed.
Thank you!

For my healers, teachers and tribe. Sass was born from these classrooms and teachings and she is a portal through which I can spread these technologies and teachings. Ho! And So, it is! Sat Nam!

For my Brother, I see you, and I love you. Cape On!

For all of us who, at times, might be afraid to feel and express our emotions but move past the fear to allow ourselves to have the full range of our human experience.

Last, but not least, for the real Mrs. Moo: You may truly never know just how significant the positive impact your true friendship has had on my family and me. Thank you for letting me sit at your kitchen table and feel my emotions. I love you.

Cape On!

A Note to Parents and Caretakers:

I'm super excited for you and your kid(s) to meet Lil' Sass and accompany her on her adventures as she learns about her emotions. This topic of both having and being with our emotions isn't always an easy one. I learned this through my own journey, which is why I wanted to create Lil' Sass: to help adults and children talk about and experience emotions in a healthy, supportive way. I hope these stories support you as much as they support your child(ren). I share this with you with deep gratitude and respect for your dedication to your role as a parent and caretaker.

Cape On!

Sincerely,

Christie Mann

Meet Lil' Sass.

She is ten years old and is independent, clever, and determined. Her real name is Grace, but ever since she was a baby, her parents have called her Lil' Sass because she is just so adventurous and curious.

Lil' Sass lives in Venice Beach, California with her Mom. She likes roller-skating, going on adventures, and making new friends. Her dad used to live with them, but he and Mom started arguing a lot, and then he left. A few days after he left, her friend, Mrs. Moo, gave her The Red Cape.

Mrs. Moo is a kind and wise older lady who rents the little house in the backyard. Her job is to help people feel things. When she gave Lil' Sass The Red Cape, she said, "Sass, you can go inside of this Cape and feel whatever you are feeling. Just say, 'Cape On!' There, inside your Cape, you can explore and express all of your emotions."

"Feeling is a gift you give yourself. It is your right as a human being to experience your emotions— all of them." Emotion is the word Mrs. Moo uses to describe feelings like anger, sadness, and joy. As Sass goes about her adventures, she explores new emotions with her Cape.

The Adventure of Anger

It was a good day to skate!
The sun was shining brightly, and Lil' Sass
could feel a cool breeze on her face.

She skated down to the roller rink to see her
friends, Mr. O.G. and Tommy. Mr. O.G. was one
of the "Original Gangsters,"
a nickname his friends gave him because he had
been roller skating in Venice Beach for so long.

He was always so kind to Lil' Sass.
He even taught her how to do dance routines
on her skates. Tommy was Sass' best friend.
He lived in the neighborhood, too, and he loved
to skate as much as Sass did!

Mr. O.G. was teaching Tommy and Lil' Sass a new routine. Tommy was really getting the moves.

He was doing the new routine much quicker and better than Sass.

Sass started to feel really hot all over. She noticed that she was having a hard time concentrating on Mr. O.G.'s instructions. It felt like an emotion needed to come out.

What was it?

Lil' Sass told O.G. and Tommy that she needed to go to the restroom, but that was not true. She still felt really hot, and it was hard to focus.

As she was skating up the path, a bicyclist came out of nowhere and almost hit her. Lil' Sass thought, "Hey! He broke the rule! He was not supposed to be on that path!"

Sass tripped and fell face first into the sand.
Now she was so hot that her skin
was turning red!

FUDGE, FUDGE, FUDGE, FU

She turned her hand pinky-side down and started karate chopping the sand.

"Cape On!"

Sass cried, and pulled her Red Cape around her.
Her whole body felt like it was burning up.
As she continued to karate chop the sand,
a thought came into her head.
"This is anger. I am angry!" Sass yelled. And then
she thought about all the things people had told
her about anger.

E, FUDGE, FUDGE!!

There was the time the teacher yelled
at Lil' Sass when she got mad at Frankie
and Sarah for hiding her skates.
Sass remembered getting really hot then,
too, and not being able to focus.

She was so mad that she yelled at Frankie
and Sarah! Her teacher ran over and said
"Lil' Sass, it's not lady-like to be angry.
Ask Frankie and Sarah nicely and calmly
for your skates."

Then there was the time when she and Grandma overheard Mom and Dad fighting. They were both talking really loudly. Her grandmother said, "Being angry is not how nice, smart people should behave. Remember that, Sass."

Lil' Sass thought about all of these things while she was tucked under her Cape in the sand.

She had been told that it was not okay to be angry. This confused her. Actually, it made her even more angry!

Sass felt angry that she was having a hard time learning the new roller skate routine, she felt angry that the boy on the bike broke the rule and caused her to fall, and suddenly, she realized that she felt really, really mad about something else, as well.

Sass wondered why it was so bad to be angry. Her anger felt natural, and she was not using it to hurt anyone else. Then she thought about the day that Mrs. Moo gave her The Red Cape.

Mrs. Moo said, "Sass, sometimes you will be so angry. You will be angry at yourself, at your parents, at other people, even angry at the world. You will feel like you could yell at the top of your lungs, 'I'M SO MAD AT YOU, WORLD!'"

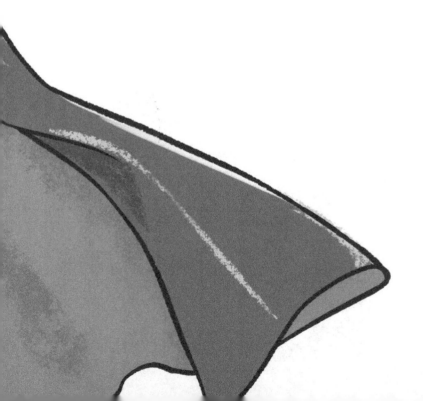

"That is okay. Let yourself do that. Use your
Red Cape to let the anger move right
through you. You can even karate chop pillows
until you have no more energy left and the anger
turns into tears. There is nothing wrong
with being angry. The key is to let the anger
out and make sure you do not let it
out on others, even if you are angry at them.
When you do this, you might even realize that
a bigger anger is hiding that little anger.
Let yourself feel this emotion. Let yourself
feel little angers to get to the bigger angers,
okay? Feeling this emotion is your right
as a human being."

At the time, Sass didn't know what Mrs. Moo was talking about, but now it was making sense. She would use her Red Cape to feel her anger. Lil' Sass noticed that she was not feeling hot anymore.

Then she realized that she was actually no longer feeling angry. She felt tired, but she felt much better, too.

Sass thought about the things people had said about anger, and realized that some of the things might not have been completely true. Sass decided that it was important to express her anger.

She now understood what Mrs. Moo was saying about little angers and big angers. Sass realized that what she was really angry about was that her dad had gone away, and she was really missing him.

She made a promise to herself that she would speak to Mrs. Moo and her mom about it when she got home. She hugged her Red Cape and felt so grateful for it.

Sass got up, wiped the sand away from her hands and knees, and skated back down to the roller rink. Sass skated right in line with Mr. O.G. and Tommy, who were still practicing the new routine. This time she got the new moves down! She sighed with relief.

She was happy to learn the new routine, but it also felt really good to know that it was okay to be angry at times, and to understand what was really bothering her, too.

With her Red Cape, she had a safe place to express her emotions.

Cape On!

Discussion Guide

Cape On, Moms, Dads and Caretakers!

Lil' Sass is here to teach your kids about feeling their emotions all the way, and empowering them to do so with confidence. But she can't do it alone! As you read through Sass' adventures, please use the following questions to stimulate discussions with your kids about their emotions and their relationship with their emotions.

I encourage you to be open by revealing some of the toughest emotions you've experienced in a way that your kids can understand. Then invite them to do the same, and be ready to hold space and support whatever comes up for them. Feeling and experiencing our emotions is a lifelong journey, and together, we can help point kids along the way. Remember what Mrs. Moo says, "Feeling emotions is our right as human beings!"

Cape On!

Questions:

- What are some of the toughest emotions you've felt? How did you handle them?

- Sass feels really angry that the dance moves are so hard. Have you ever felt angry about something being hard?

- Sass got even more angry when the bicyclist broke the rules! How do you feel when other kids break the rules?

- After Sass allows herself to feel her anger, she realizes that the little angers are covering up a bigger anger. Has that ever happened to you?

- Have you ever felt so angry you wanted to karate chop something? Let's do something silly: let's try to karate chop a pillow together right now! How did that feel?

- Are there things you should not karate chop or punch, even if you're feeling really, really angry?

- Sass gets hot when she is angry. What happens in your body when you're angry?

- What are you learning about emotions?

READY TO CAPE ON?

Visit the Sass Shop to get a cape
for Mom, Dad, caretakers and kiddos!

FREE BONUSES!

Discover free bonuses for Lil' Sass readers!
Visit www.lilsass.com

EXPLORE MORE BOOKS
by Christie Mann

#CAPEON

About the Author

Christie Mann has made it her mission to be an 'ever-student' to fulfill her purpose of being a leader who develops leaders, who develop leaders. Christie is an author, spiritual psychologist, leadership coach, learning consultant, trainer, speaker and Kundalini Yoga & Meditation teacher who designs and facilitates transformational content and experiences that make our world a happier, healthier and more connected place to be.

At 13-years-old, Christie's life suddenly and dramatically shifted when she suffered some devastating losses and was thrust into a leadership position, which subsequently, impacted her relationship with her own emotional growth. She has spent the better part of the past two decades on her own corrective path and, because of this, has a sincere desire to encourage others to have a healthier and more responsible relationship with their emotions.

She is the creator of The Adventures of Lil' Sass, a series of personal development books for young people, accompanied by supporting accessories & experiences – a brand that teaches the importance and value of being with our own emotions and shows us how much JOY we can experience when we allow ourselves to be fully self-expressed. She draws inspiration for the characters, stories and accessories from her own life experiences and her learnings from Therapy, the Co-Active methodology through CTI, a Master's Degree in the Practices and Principles of Spiritual Psychology from the University of Santa Monica, and her practice of the ancient technology of Kundalini Yoga. Christie also obtained an Undergraduate-Degree in Media, Information and Technoculture from the University of Western Ontario.

Originally from a small town in Ontario, Canada, Christie now lives in Venice Beach, California where you can find her at the Venice Roller Rink, the sunny shores of the Santa Monica Pier or at RAMA, a local Kundalini Yoga studio. An Auntie many times over, she's in awe of children's resilience and emotional flexibility and champions adults' rights to have and express emotions too.

Cape On!

A Deeper Cut on the Dedication & Acknowledgements

For all the little hearts in my life: Carson, Mia, Kingston, Cee Cee, Abbey, Will, Sebby, Hugo, Willow, Tommy, Jake, Lily, Brooks, Biba, Ma'ila, Rafi, Benji, Ellis, Althea, Alec, Mavis, Véronique, Freddy, Camille, Nik, Oliver, Luke, Gen, Gabby, Sophia, Reese, Tessa, Chloe, Mila, Jamie, Nathan, Noora & Israa. Watching you grow is one of my greatest joys, and it inspired me to write this series and create this brand. And for your mothers and fathers - because without them you would not be here and neither would Sass. And for D, for reigniting the spark of Sass in me - so she could be birthed.

Thank you to my dear friends, whom I call family. And to my dear family, whom I call friends.

For my healers, teachers and tribe. For Katherine Belfontaine for being the first one to make it safe to express my emotions—all of them. For Henry, Karen and Laura for birthing CTI/Co-Active and my Co-Active Family for creating experiences and circles where I am safe to go deeper and share more of my authentic self. For John: Thank you for your grace, equanimity and unconditional love. For my Purple Hearts, Teachers Ron and Mary Hulnick, and the practices and principles of Spiritual Psychology from USM. For Pam, thank you for helping me heal my body and introducing me to Melinda to heal on other planes. For Birch, you are a goddess and a magician. For Britta and Lee Eskey and the deep healing and courageous expression of ALL emotions through the COR experiences and brave community. For my community of Yogis and Teachers: Hawijian, Tej, Guru Jagat, Gurujas, Jai Gopal, Raghubir and the study and practice of Kundalini Yoga. Sass was born from these classrooms and she is a portal through which I can spread these technologies and teachings. Ho! And So, it is! Sat Nam!

For Pops, Momma and Stuy, I see you and I love you. Cape On!

For all of us who at times might be afraid to feel and express our emotions but, regardless, move past the fear to allow ourselves to truly have the full range of our human experience.

Last, but not least, for the real Mrs. Moo: You may truly never know just how significant the positive impact your true friendship has had on me and my family. Thank you for letting me sit at your kitchen table and feel my emotions. I love you.

Cape On!